Developing Lit[e]

NON-FICTION

READING AND WRITING
ACTIVITIES FOR THE LITERACY HOUR

year

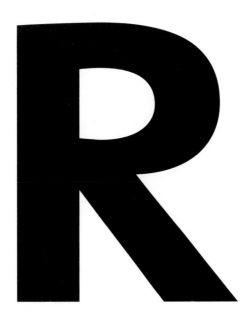

Christine Moorcroft

Series consultant: Ray Barker

A & C BLACK

Contents

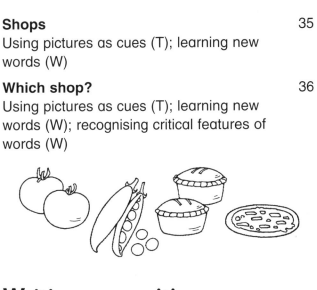

Writing composition

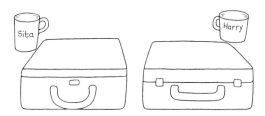

Acknowledgements
This book is dedicated to the memory of Leon Baxter.

Reprinted 2002
Published 2002 by
A & C Black Publishers Limited
37 Soho Square, London W1D 3QZ
www.acblack.com

ISBN 0-7136-6058-9

The author and publishers would like to thank Ray Barker, Madeleine Madden, Julia Tappin and Sarah Vickers for their advice in producing this series of books.

A CIP catalogue record for this book is available from the British Library.

A & C Black uses paper produced with elemental chlorine-free pulp, harvested from managed sustainable forests.
Printed in Great Britain by Cromwell Press Ltd, Trowbridge, Wiltshire.

Introduction

Developing Literacy: Non-fiction is a series of seven photocopiable activity books for the Literacy Hour. Each book provides a range of non-fiction reading and writing activities, and supports the teaching of reading and writing skills at text, sentence and word levels.

The activities are designed to be carried out in the time allocated to independent work and incorporate strategies that encourage independent learning – for example, ways in which children can evaluate their own work or that of a partner.

The reading activities develop the children's study and research skills (reading for a purpose, understanding and interpreting, and making use of what they have read) and provide models on which they can base their own writing.

The writing activities concentrate on the purpose of a text, the audience for whom it is written and the context in which it is to be read, and encourage the children to be aware of these considerations when they write.

Most children will be able to carry out the activities on their own, but it is assumed that an adult will read the instructions to or with the younger children.

The activities in **Year R** encourage the children to:

- recognise printed and handwritten text in different settings, understand its purpose and use cues which help them to read and understand text;
- learn about the conventions of text and the vocabulary used in talking about books;
- understand how letters and words make up text and how text differs from pictures;
- locate and use significant parts of a text;
- use writing for different purposes;
- plan their writing;
- model their writing on written texts.

The National Literacy Strategy and non-fiction

The National Literacy Strategy *Framework for Teaching* encourages teachers to use all kinds of non-fiction texts, both printed and electronic: for example, signs and directions; lists; information books and dictionaries; labels and captions in the classroom; and instructions which the children follow at school, at home and elsewhere.

Links to other subjects

The children can use their literacy skills to further their learning in other subjects, through the reading of shared texts or guided reading during the Literacy Hour and by using their developing research skills. During the Literacy Hour, the children could write about what they have encountered in other subjects and learn how to select the best methods for writing about what they have learned.

Using non-fiction in the Literacy Hour

While the activities in this book focus on the independent part of the Literacy Hour, the notes on pages 5 to 8 and at the foot of each activity page suggest a variety of ways you can introduce non-fiction reading and writing, present whole-class activities and use the plenary session to conclude the lesson. The ideas support the following strategies:

- **demonstrating** or modelling the way in which an experienced reader and writer tackles a skill or approach to reading or writing, by 'thinking aloud' about what you are doing;
- **sharing** an activity so that the teacher or other adult (as the expert) takes responsibility for the difficult parts of the activity, while the learners take responsibility for the easier parts. The learners then gradually take over some of the more difficult parts. This bridges the gap between demonstration and independent work;
- **supporting** an activity, in which the children undertake the activity independently, with the teacher (or other adult) monitoring and being ready to offer support when necessary. This avoids the difficulties which arise when the teacher moves from demonstration or modelling to asking the children to work independently.

Teachers are encouraged to help the children to read and write non-fiction by:

- **predicting** (suggesting what information a book or page might provide, and how you can tell);
- **clarifying** (helping children to work out ways to understand new or difficult words and ideas);
- **questioning** (saying what questions the text raises – what it makes you want to find out);
- **summarising** (saying in a limited number of words what the text is about and what it tells you).

The activities in this book support the following stages of the children's interactions with text:

- **bringing to mind what they already know** about the subject (for example, making diagrams and lists);

- **deciding what they want to find out** (for example, writing questions);

- **deciding where to find the information** (for example, information books, electronic texts, people and websites);

- **learning the best ways in which to use the source** (from the teacher or other adult, who models the use of the source);

- **developing strategies to help them to understand the text** (for example, marking difficult words or passages, re-phrasing, or transferring information from prose to charts or from diagrams to prose);

- **recording information** (using note-making strategies such as abbreviation and charts);

- **evaluating the information** (for example, evaluating the validity of the source or comparing information on the same topic from different sources, and separating fact from opinion);

- **communicating information** (considering the audience, purpose and context of the text to be written and their effects on language, layout and other features).

Organisation

The activities require very few resources besides scissors, glue, word-banks and simple dictionaries. Other materials are specified in the teachers' notes on the activity pages.

Extension activities

Most of the activity sheets end with a challenge (**Now try this!**) which reinforces and extends the children's learning and provides the teacher with an opportunity for assessment. These more challenging activities might be appropriate for only a few children; it is not expected that the whole class should complete all of them. On some pages there is space for the children to complete the extension activities, but others will require a notebook or a separate sheet of paper.

The notes below expand upon those which are provided at the foot of each activity page. They give ideas and suggestions for making the most of the activity sheet, including suggestions for the whole-class introduction, the plenary session or for follow-up work using an adapted version of the activity sheet. To help teachers select appropriate learning experiences for their pupils, the activities are grouped into sections within each book, but the pages need not be presented in the order in which they appear, unless otherwise stated.

Understanding of print: reading

The activities in this section develop the children's skills in the following areas: recognising printed and handwritten words in a variety of settings; understanding that words can be written down to be read again, for a range of purposes; recognising and understanding terms used about books and print; learning how to track text in the correct direction (left to right and top to bottom); and encouraging them to point to the words they are reading and make one-to-one correspondences between written and spoken words.

Giving presents (page 9). This text-level activity provides practice in recognising handwritten words in different settings: in this instance, a collection of labelled presents. It also develops word-level skills in learning to read on sight the high-frequency words 'to' and 'from'. The activity could be linked with work in personal and social development, with the children giving 'friendship' presents to children in another class (they could wrap a piece of fruit and write a label for the present). Alternatively, bring a teddy bear to school and tell the children it is the teddy bear's birthday: they could wrap and label presents and make birthday cards for it.

Sorting coats (page 10). This activity develops the children's text-level skills in recognising words in different settings and understanding that words can be written down to be read for different purposes. The activity could be linked with the children's personal and social development: taking care of their own property and that of others. Ask the children to read the name labels on their own belongings and discuss the purpose of these labels. Groups of children could read name labels on clothes and match the clothes to their owners. As a further extension activity, they could make name labels for dolls' clothes.

Spot the animals (page 11). This activity can be used to show the children how to record their observations in other subjects, such as science, and on class outings. In the extension activity, other farm animals they could draw and whose names they could write are pig, goose and goat. They might suggest 'chick' or 'lamb': this could be linked with vocabulary development and with work in science on the names of young animals.

Let's go! and **I spy** (pages 12–13). These activities develop the understanding that text is read from left to right. For further writing practice, the children could re-write the sentences substituting their own name for 'Anita' or 'Jack'.

Toy car (page 14). This is a simple recount of the kind the children could be helped to write in design and technology lessons. Encourage them to read the text to a partner, pointing to each word as they read it, while the partner watches. The extension activity focuses on the skill of identifying separate words.

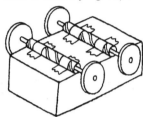

Sorting postcards (page 15). Here the children learn to recognise handwritten and printed words in different contexts. This could be linked with work on the post office: set up a school postbox and organise groups of children to take turns sorting the mail for different classes. Postcards, rather than letters, are used in this activity to avoid any confusion between the two different meanings of 'letter'. The two meanings of 'letter' could be discussed as a class.

Come and buy! (page 16). This activity develops the children's skills in recognising words in different settings. It also involves learning to read on sight the high-frequency word 'for'. In the extension activity they might find the high-frequency words 'the' or 'of', or the words for numbers. This could be linked with work in mathematics: recognising numbers and the words for numbers. The children could also look at real advertisements or promotional leaflets, signs or posters and search for any words they know.

Here is the news: 1 and 2 (pages 17–18). These activities provide practise in recognising known words in different settings. They also encourage the children to read on sight the high-frequency words 'big', 'look', 'up' and 'and'. Provide opportunities for the children to look at real newspaper headlines and search among words which they might not be able to read for any words they do know. Ask different groups of children to look for specific words which they can cut out and glue on to a large sheet of paper. Display the word collections and discuss the different kinds of print with the class.

Shopping list (page 19). This activity aims to develop the children's understanding of one of the purposes of writing: as an aid to memory. The children might not be able to read all the words, but they can use the pictures as prompts and can match the words with those on the list. They could also write shopping lists for a class shop, for a recipe or for making a model or other item in their design and technology work.

Understanding of print: writing

These activities help the children to distinguish between writing and drawing and to notice that writing is made up of separate words, each of which is made up of letters. From the activities the children learn to write for different purposes, such as sending messages, giving information and recounting, and they learn that writing is constant: it always 'says' the same thing. The children are encouraged to make their own attempts at writing new words by applying their knowledge of letter/sound correspondences.

Balloons and **Mugs** (pages 20–21). These activities provide a familiar context in which the children can distinguish writing from pictures. You could inflate commercially produced or hand-decorated balloons and ask the children to sort them into those which have writing on them and those which do not.

Lost letters: 1, 2 and 3 (pages 22–24). These activities require the children to identify the letters which make up words. The words are taken from the high-frequency list recommended by the *Framework for Teaching* for Year R. These worksheets are arranged progressively in order of difficulty and are intended to be given to the children in this order. As an extension activity, the children could take part in 'Word hunts' in which they have to find, in different contexts and media (such as magnetic letters fixed to a magnetic board, or letter tiles from a Scrabble set), the letters which make up these and other words, including their names. Some children might be able to find words hidden within other words: for example, 'it' in 'Mrs Smith', 'at' in 'Katy' and 'In' or 'it' in 'Indajit'.

Get well soon (page 25). This activity provides a format on which the children can write for a purpose: to send good wishes to someone they know who is ill. You could ask the children, 'What will the person read when he or she receives the message?' The children answer by reading back what they have written.

Write a fax (page 26). This is a simple printed form on which the children can write their own messages. It could be used in a writing corner set up as an 'office': provide copies of the page in a tray beside a pretend fax machine (or a real, disconnected one). The class could also write a fax, as a shared writing activity, to send a message to another school or to write for information on a topic. Writing a fax provides an opportunity for the children to practise using capital letters and writing their own and other people's names.

Spelling robots: 1 and **2** (pages 27–28). These activities help the children to develop strategies for spelling new words by 'sounding' the phonemes separately and then writing the letters which represent those phonemes. Using the tone of voice of a robot, the teacher could say the sounds which make up a word, ask the children what the robot is trying to say and then ask them to write the letters. A model 'spelling robot' could be displayed, with a new word to be spelled each day.

Reading comprehension

The activities in this section provide opportunities for the children to read non-fiction texts, as well as encouraging them to read other non-fiction texts which they see around them at school, at home and in the wider environment. Children learn that these texts are written for a purpose, and are encouraged to try to make sense of everyday texts by using all the available cues (pictures, sense and context as well as the shapes of words and other distinctive features), and by using their developing knowledge of grapheme/ phoneme correspondences.

In the classroom: 1 and **2** (pages 29–30). These activities are linked with everyday non-fiction texts in the classroom. You could ask the children to bring in containers with printed labels. Before the lesson, ask them to say what is inside the containers and how they know. The children could also read labelled containers in the classroom and sort a collection of items into the correct containers. Allow them to make their own labels for other containers.

What's the weather? (page 31). This activity provides practice in reading high-frequency words, including the days of the week. It could be linked with work in knowledge and understanding of the world or geography (describing the weather). Ask children to write about their own observations of the weather, in the form of either a chart and symbols or sentences. They could predict the weather for the following week and then record how accurate their predictions were.

Pond or wood? (page 32). This activity develops the children's skills in reading for information. This could be linked with work in science or knowledge and understanding of the world. The children can also read information books about animals and, with help, make charts on which to record the habitats.

Push and pull (page 33). This activity develops the children's skills in reading for information. This could be linked with work in science or knowledge and understanding of the world. Using similar charts, the children could record their investigations into pushing and pulling.

Night and day (page 34). This activity develops the children's skills in reading for information and in distinguishing between information books and stories. This could be linked with work in science or knowledge and understanding of the world.

Shops and **Which shop?** (pages 35–36). These activities could be linked with the use of a 'supermarket' role-play area in which the children can create sections for different kinds of food and write labels for the sections and the foods. To extend the activity they could sort collections of real foods (or their packets, or replica 'play' foods) into sets labelled 'bakery', 'greengrocer's', 'pet shop', 'sweetshop' and so on. For a classroom display, let the children sort pictures of goods according to the shops (or supermarket sections) in which they are sold. Encourage them to label the pictures.

Writing composition

These activities encourage the children to explore writing for different purposes, such as simple recounts, captions for pictures, labels on pictures and sentences about pictures. They learn to think about what they are going to write before they begin writing and, afterwards, to check their writing for sense.

At the pond and **At the beach** (pages 37–38). These activities encourage the children to think about the sense of a text as they read it. They could also re-read their own writing (or one another's) and check it for sense. The texts can be used as models for writing simple recounts.

Lunch boxes (page 39). This activity is linked with the children's everyday experiences of non-fiction texts. Point out that a label helps to distinguish one otherwise identical item from another. Ask the children if they can spot which two lunch boxes on the activity page are exactly the same. Each group could be given a set of labelled lunch boxes belonging to other children and asked to match them to names written on cards. They could look for names of their friends (noticing the capital letters) on the class register, on displays and on labelled items such as clothing and books.

Planting seeds (page 40). The aim of this activity is to encourage the children to think about what they will write before they write it. This could be linked with work in knowledge and understanding of the world; creative development; science; or design and technology. Children could write and illustrate instructions for other things they make or do in school: for example, baking, making models, carrying out an investigation or making a collage or print. This prepares them for later work on writing instructions.

Make a list (page 41). This activity can be used to support the development of the children's planning skills. Discuss with them what Jane is going to do and ask them to think of all the things she will need. Talk about the way in which a list is used: it is written to be read again later, in order to remember things or actions. Revise the format of a list: it is written from top to bottom. You could make long, narrow notepads on which the children can write other lists.

Take a seat and **Have a drink** (pages 42–43). These activities develop the children's skills in reading for information and then recording what they have found out. This could be linked with work in history or knowledge and understanding of the world: the children could observe and draw objects used in the past and then label their drawings and write sentences about the objects. Examples of suitable objects include a flat iron, a warming pan, an earthenware hot-water bottle, a washtub or a washboard.

House labels (page 44). You could link this activity with work on homes. The children first need to learn the vocabulary for parts of a house. They could use information books to find out about different houses and homes which they draw and label. Some children might be able to use information books to find the words for, and then label, other details in their drawings, such as 'step', 'chimney', 'garage', 'letterbox' and 'path'.

All about me (page 45). This activity supports the children in writing to give information (about themselves). You could first show the children examples of forms and discuss any forms they have seen people filling in. Discuss the purpose of forms, i.e. to give information. Forms could be introduced into several types of role-play, such as dentist's surgery, hospital, doctor's surgery, hotel, restaurant, bank, post office or estate agent. Provide authentic forms on which the children can write during their role-play.

Where are they going?: 1 and 2 (pages 46–47). These activities provide sentences with a repeated format for the children to follow. They could be used in conjunction with a fiction text in which directional words and other words for movement are used: for example, *Cat Among the Cabbages* (Alison Bartlett, Levinson), *We're Going on a Bear Hunt* (Michael Rosen, Walker) or *We're Going on a Dragon Hunt* (Maurice Jones, Puffin). During a whole-class activity, you could perform an action and ask the children, 'Where am I going?' The children respond with a sentence: for example, 'You are going up the steps'.

Alternatively, they could choose an action to perform which involves movement up, down, over or along and then make up a sentence to describe it: for example, 'I am going along the carpet'. The teacher or another adult could scribe the sentence, with the child writing as much of it as possible. Invite contributions from other children. Ask the child to re-read the sentence to check that it makes sense.

In the picture (page 48). This activity can be linked with work in any subject. Encourage the children to talk about the pictures, saying what they can see. Some children could write a short sentence such as, 'This is a ladybird', while others might be able to write a longer sentence which says where the animal is: for example, 'I can see a ladybird on a twig'. Revise the spellings of the high-frequency words 'this', 'here', 'is', 'can' and 'see'. To encourage the children to write captions, display a picture at a suitable height in the classroom along with a large sheet of blank paper. Invite children to write captions for the picture. At the end of a day or a week the captions could be read aloud.

Giving presents

- **Ring** (To) **in green.**
- **Ring** (from) **in yellow.**

To Karl
from Meg

To Rani
from John

To Sam
from Ben

To Raj
from Anna

To Kim from Dan

To Tom from Dev

- **Draw presents for three other people.**
- **Write** | labels |.

  Use | To | **and** | from |.

Now try this!

Teachers' note As a shared reading activity, read enlarged handwritten labels for presents to and
from different people; discuss the words which appear on all the labels ('to' and 'from') and point out the
different ways in which they can be written (sometimes beginning with upper-case letters and sometimes
with lower-case letters).

**Developing Literacy
Non-fiction Year R
© A & C Black 2002**

Sorting coats

- **Join the children to their coats.**

- **Make labels for three of your friends.**

Now try this!

Teachers' note Before the lesson, you could copy and enlarge labels from children's belongings. Read them as shared texts and ask the children to identify their own name labels. Show them labels for the same name used for different purposes: for example, labelling on clothing, cloakroom hooks, lunch boxes or books.

Developing Literacy
Non-fiction Year R
© A & C Black 2002

Spot the animals

- **Read the** list **.**
- **Tick the animals you can see.** ✓

dog

cat ✓
cow ☐
dog ☐
duck ☐
hen ☐
horse ☐
mouse ☐
rat ☐
sheep ☐

sheep

duck

hen

cow

horse

cat

- **Draw three other farm animals.**
- **Write labels for them.**

Now try this!

Use information books.

Teachers' note Introduce the activity using a shared text, such as a poster, for which you have made a large-size checklist for the children to mark. This could be linked with work in science (the poster could show, for example, a pond or woodlands). The children could use information books to help them to write their own checklists of animals or plants for use during a nature walk.

Developing Literacy
Non-fiction Year R
© A & C Black 2002

Let's go!

- **Write the missing** words **in the** sentences .
- **Trace the arrows.**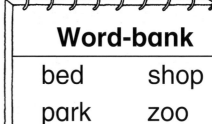

Word-bank

bed	shop
park	zoo

 Anita goes to school.

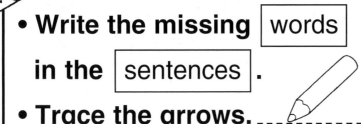

 Anita goes to the _____.

 Anita goes to _____ _____.

 Anita goes _____ _____ _____.

 _____ _____ _____ _____.

- **Write about where you go.**
- **Draw pictures.**

Teachers' note Encourage the children to follow the arrows with a finger while they read the words. They could do the same as they read other texts. They could also have fun reading the words of the sentences in a different order: for example, 'school goes to Anita'. Ask them if the sentences mean the same when the words are read in a different order.

Developing Literacy Non-fiction Year R © A & C Black 2002

I spy

- **Write the missing words in the sentences.**
- **Trace the arrows.**

Word-bank

bat	dog
cat	pig

Jack sees an elephant.

——————————————→

Jack sees a _____.

- - - - - - - - - - - - - →

Jack sees _____ _____.

- - - - - - - - - - - - - →

Jack _____ ___ _____.

- - - - - - - - - - - - - →

_____ _____ ___ _____.

- - - - - - - - - - - - - →

Now try this!

- **Write about things you see at school.**
- **Draw pictures.**

Teachers' note Encourage the children to follow the arrows with a finger while they read the words. They could do the same as they read other texts. They could also have fun reading the words of the sentences in a different order: for example, 'an elephant sees Jack'. Ask them if the sentences mean the same when the words are read in a different order.

Developing Literacy
Non-fiction Year R
© A & C Black 2002

Toy car

- **Read about making a toy car.**

This is how I made a car.

I took a box.

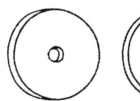

I took four wheels.

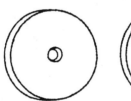 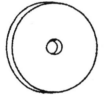

I took two straws.

I took two sticks.

I put the wheels on the box.

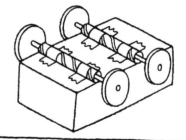

 • Ring each word.

Teachers' note Encourage the children to use the pictures as cues when they attempt any words they cannot read: for example, 'straws' and 'sticks'. They could use this page as a model to help them to write a recount of an activity such as making a model or carrying out an investigation. The extension activity focuses on the identification of separate words in a text.

Developing Literacy
Non-fiction Year R
© A & C Black 2002

14

Sorting postcards

• **Colour the children's postcards.**

Meg Penn — blue

Raj Vazi — green

Sam Bell — yellow

Simi Ogini — red

School post box

Meg Penn Class R

Simi Ogini Class I

Sam Bell Class I

Raj Vazi Class R

Raj Vazi Class R

Sam Bell Class I

Meg Penn Class R

Simi Ogini Class I

Now try this!

• **Write your friend's name and class on a postcard.**

Teachers' note Suggest to the children that they first colour the labels at the top of the page as a reminder. You could make some large 'postcards' to read as shared texts (they could be addressed to various people in the school). This can be linked with a class post office: ask how the children whose turn it is to sort and deliver the post will know to whom the cards and letters should go.

**Developing Literacy
Non-fiction Year R
© A & C Black 2002**

15

Come and buy!

- **Ring** (for) **in red.**

Two for
10p

Three for
the price
of two

Two for
the price
of one

Sale – for
one day only!

Six sweets for
five pence

Five jars
for £1

Now try
this!

- **Find another word you**

  know.

- **Write the word.**

Teachers' note To introduce this activity you could collect and display advertisements (in sufficiently large text) which contain words or letters the children know. Fix a sheet of paper next to each advertisement and invite the children to copy on to it any words in the advertisement that they can read.

**Developing Literacy
Non-fiction Year R
© A & C Black 2002**

• Ring the word (big) in blue.

The big
match

Big shock

My big dog

Win big prizes

The big
storm

The big paper
for BIG news

Now try this!

• Find two other words
you know.

• Write the words in
the box.

Teachers' note To introduce this activity you could collect and display newspaper headlines which contain words the children know. Fix a sheet of paper next to each headline and invite the children to copy on to it any words in the headline that they can read. They could practise writing the same words in upper- and lower-case letters. See also page 18.

Developing Literacy
Non-fiction Year R
© A & C Black 2002

Here is the news 2

- **Ring these words.**

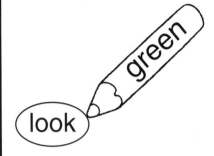 look — green

 up — red

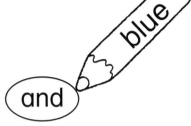 and — blue

NEWS

Stray dogs and cats are safe.

NEWS

Bus fares go up.

NEWS

The road up the hill is blocked.

NEWS

Police look for lost boy.

NEWS

Snow and ice

NEWS

Look out for this man.

- **Tick the words which are on the newspapers?** ✓

go ☐   the ☐   for ☐

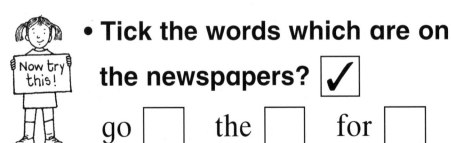

Teachers' note The children could bring in newspaper headlines containing words they can read. During a whole-class activity a collection of headlines could be displayed. Invite the children to read them, looking for words they know or words from the high-frequency list. See also page 17.

**Developing Literacy
Non-fiction Year R
© A & C Black 2002**

Shopping list

Dad writes a shopping list.

- **Read the shopping list.**

bananas
bread
cakes
eggs
fish
grapes
peas
soup

- **Tick the things Dad needs to buy.**

chicken ☐

eggs ☐

fish ☐

bread ☐

cakes ☐

peas ☐

soup ☐

apples ☐

grapes ☐

bananas ☐

Now try this!

- **Write another shopping list. Draw pictures.**
- **Give your list to a friend to read.**

Teachers' note During a whole-class activity you could set up a table with labelled items of shopping, and display a 'shopping list'. Ask the children to read the list (using the labelled shopping to help them) and invite them to tick the items as they put each one into a shopping basket. Discuss the way in which a shopping list is written – with the items one beneath the other, rather than across the page.

Developing Literacy
Non-fiction Year R
© A & C Black 2002

19

Balloons

• **Tick the balloons with** writing **on them.** ✔

Good luck

Happy birthday

New baby

New home

Now try this!

• **Draw a balloon with a** picture **on it.**
• **Draw a balloon with** writing **on it.**

Teachers' note Ask the children if they can read any of the words on the balloons and discuss the occasions when people might display them. The children could design their own balloons for particular occasions and say what they are going to write on them. You could provide a word-bank of 'greetings' words.

Developing Literacy
Non-fiction Year R
© A & C Black 2002

Mugs

• **Colour the mugs with writing on them.**

• **Draw a mug with a** pattern **on it.**

• **Draw a mug with writing on it.**

Teachers' note You could collect and display mugs, some with writing and some without. Ask the children to sort the mugs into sets: 'Writing' and 'No writing'. Help them to read the writing on the mugs.

**Developing Literacy
Non-fiction Year R
© A & C Black 2002**

Lost letters 1

- **Read the word in the box.**

- **Find the** letters **.**

- **Trace the letters.**

Use a different colour for each word.

| on |

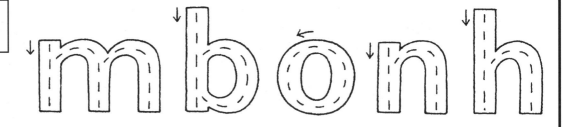

| at |

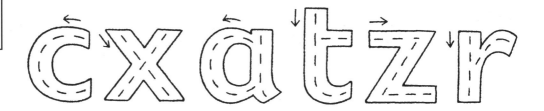

| is |

| up |

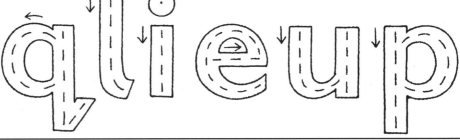

- **Look at the letters.** z   t   c   o   u

- **Find a word.**

- **Write the word.**

Teachers' note The children could first practise finding the letters (from sets of plastic or wooden letters) which make up these words and other short words they know. Each group could be allocated a word to find from a selection of letters. For the extension activity, explain that the letters of the word are mixed up with other letters. See also pages 23 and 24.

Developing Literacy Non-fiction Year R © A & C Black 2002

Lost letters 2

- **Read the word in the box.**
- **Find the letters.**
- **Trace the letters.**

Use a different colour for each word.

big	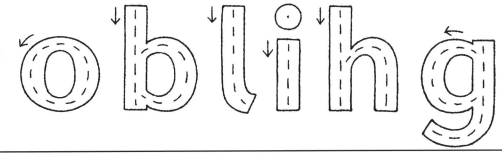

for	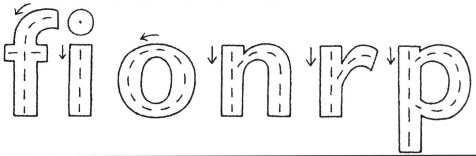

the	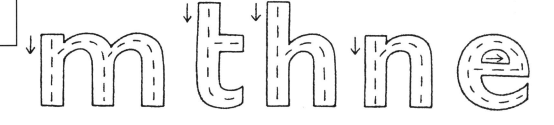

you	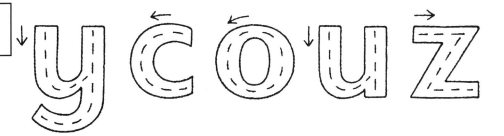

- **Look at the letters.**   n y o e s
- **Find two words.**
- **Write the words.**

Teachers' note You could set up a 'word corner' in which the words on this page and on pages 22 and 24 are written on a sheet of paper; provide a set of plastic letters from which the children can make up the words. Ensure the children understand that the letters of the words are interspersed with other letters in this activity.

Developing Literacy
Non-fiction Year R
© A & C Black 2002

- **Read the word in the box.**

- **Find the letters.**

- **Trace the letters.**

Use a different colour for each word.

| this | 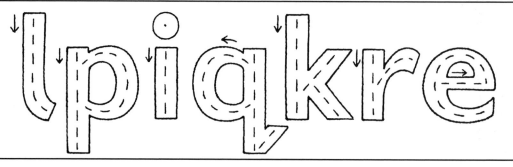 |

| like | 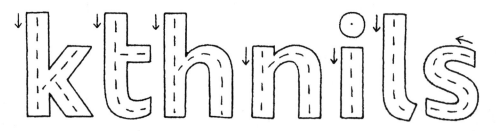 |

| went | 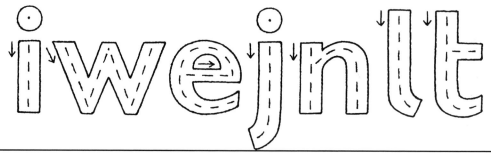 |

| said |  |

- **Look at the letters.**
- **Find two words.**
- **Write the words.**

| c | o | u | m | s | e |

Teachers' note The children should first complete the activities on pages 22 and 23. Ensure the children understand that the letters of the words are interspersed with other letters.

Developing Literacy Non-fiction Year R © A & C Black 2002

Get well soon

• **Write a** message **to someone who is not well.**

Use words from the word-bank to help you.

Word-bank

Dear
love
from

Teachers' note This activity could be introduced by reading an enlarged Get well card as a shared text. Help the children to read the front cover and the message. Discuss the purpose of a Get well card and ask the children what message they want to send to someone who is ill.

**Developing Literacy
Non-fiction Year R**
© A & C Black 2002

Write a fax

Fax to	Fax from
_____	_____
_____	_____
Fax number	Fax number
_____	_____

Message

_____

_____

_____

_____

_____

Teachers' note Show the children (in small groups, if necessary) how the school fax machine works and ask if any of them has used one or if they have one at home. Discuss how it is used and how people know who has sent the fax and to what number they should reply. Then invite the children to write their own fax on this form. Emphasise that a fax message is written for someone else to read and reply to.

Developing Literacy
Non-fiction Year R
© A & C Black 2002

- **Look at the picture.**
- **Say the word.**
- **Write the word.**

t	a	p

tap

h	e	n

_____

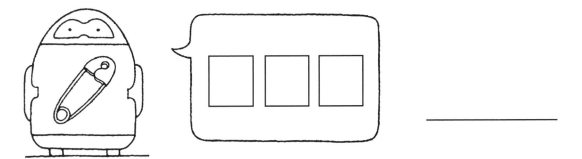

☐ ☐ ☐

_____

☐ ☐ ☐

_____

 **• Draw spelling robots for these.**

Now try this!

Teachers' note You could introduce the activity by holding up a picture and asking the children what it is (begin with simple consonant-vowel-consonant words). Invite a child to be a 'spelling robot' (perhaps dressing up in a simple 'robot' suit) and to say the sounds which make up the word, while another child writes the letters or points to them on an alphabet strip. See also page 28.

**Developing Literacy
Non-fiction Year R
© A & C Black 2002**

Spelling robots 2

b | u | sh _____

d | i | sh _____

☐ ☐ ☐ _____

☐ ☐ ☐ _____

Now try this! • **Draw spelling robots for these.**

Teachers' note The children should first complete the activity on page 27. Introduce the activity by holding up a picture and asking the children what it is (use words containing 'sh'). Invite a child to be a 'spelling robot' and to say the sounds which make up the word, while another child writes the letters or points to them on an alphabet strip. Extend the activity to include words containing other phonemes.

Developing Literacy
Non-fiction Year R
© A & C Black 2002

In the classroom 1

pencils

paintbrushes

rulers

cubes

shells

scissors

beads

Teachers' note Cut out the cards on this page and on page 30. Read the words with the children and ask them to match the objects to the labelled containers. For children who can match the objects to the containers by the words alone, the pictures on this page could be masked before copying. Continued on page 30.

Developing Literacy
Non-fiction Year R
© A & C Black 2002

In the classroom 2

pencils

paintbrushes

rulers

cubes

shells

scissors

beads

Teachers' note Continued from page 29. As an extension activity, the children could write labels for some of the containers they use at school, or they could draw pictures of containers and write labels for them. A poster-sized, illustrated word-bank could be provided for reference.

Developing Literacy
Non-fiction Year R
© A & C Black 2002

What's the weather?

• **Read the** chart .

Monday	(snowman)
Tuesday	(foggy lines)
Wednesday	(cloud)
Thursday	(rain and leaves)
Friday	(sun and leaves)

Use the key to help you.

Key

cloudy (cloud)

foggy (foggy lines)

rainy (raindrops)

sunny (sun)

snowy (snowman)

windy (leaves)

• **Write the missing words.**

On Monday it was _____.

On Tuesday it was _____.

On Wednesday _____.

On _____ it was rainy and windy.

• **Write a sentence about the weather on Friday.**

Look at the key.

Teachers' note A large weather display-board could be read as a shared text, with the emphasis on using cues (such as the initial phoneme, a picture or a memorised sequence such as the days of the week) to read unknown words. Introduce the term 'key' and explain what a key is for.

Developing Literacy
Non-fiction Year R
© A & C Black 2002

Pond or wood?

- **Look at the pictures.**

- **Read the words.**

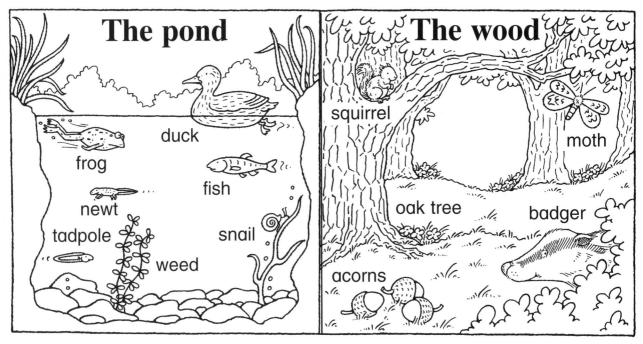

- **Write where the things live.**

Write | pond | **or** | wood | .

acorn	wood	newt	
badger		oak tree	
duck		snail	
fish		squirrel	
frog		tadpole	
moth		weed	

- **Draw something else that lives in a pond.**

- **Write a label.**

Use information books.

Teachers' note This could be enlarged and read as a shared text, with the emphasis on using cues to read unknown words. The activity involves reading labels in order to gather information. The charts enable the children to record this information in a different way and allow the teacher to assess their understanding of the text.

Developing Literacy
Non-fiction Year R
© A & C Black 2002

Push and pull

• **Look at the pictures. Read the words.**

You push a pram.

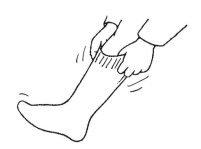

You pull up socks.

You pull a sledge.

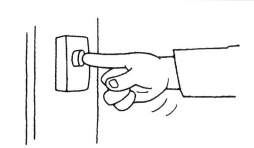

You push a doorbell.

• **What do you do? Write** push **or** pull .

pram		push
socks		
sledge		
doorbell		

• **Draw something you push.**

• **Draw something you pull.**

• **Write labels for your drawings.**

Teachers' note This could be introduced as a shared or guided reading activity. It involves reading the text in order to gather information. The charts enable the children to record this information in a different way and allow the teacher to assess their understanding of the text. Some children might be able to draw and label things which can be both pushed and pulled (such as a door or a drawer).

Developing Literacy
Non-fiction Year R
© A & C Black 2002

Night and day

• **Look at the pictures. Read the words.**

  Some animals sleep at night.
Some animals sleep in the day.

 An owl sleeps in the day.

A dog sleeps at night.

A hamster sleeps in the day.

A horse sleeps at night.

A cow sleeps at night.

• **When do they sleep. Write** | night | **or** | day |.

cow		*night*
dog		
hamster		
horse		
owl		

Now try this!

• **Find out when other animals sleep.**

Use information books.

• **Make a chart to write on.**

Teachers' note This could be introduced by writing the two introductory sentences on a board and reading them with the children, with the emphasis on the words which are repeated in the rest of the text (animals, sleep/sleeps, night and day). If possible, read a shared text about nocturnal and diurnal animals and provide information books which the children can read.

Developing Literacy
Non-fiction Year R
© A & C Black 2002

Shops

The bakery

buns

cakes

pies

pizzas

naan breads

The greengrocer's

tomatoes

peas

carrots

potatoes

potatoes

turnips

Teachers' note Use this with page 36. Discuss the two types of shop (or the corresponding sections of a supermarket) and ask the children to name any foods they have seen there. Enlarge the page and read it with the children.

**Developing Literacy
Non-fiction Year R
© A & C Black 2002**

The bakery

The greengrocer's

	tomatoes		buns
	peas		cakes
	carrots		pies
	potatoes	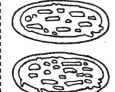	pizzas
	turnips		naan breads

Teachers' note Continued from page 35. Cut out the cards. The children can glue each shop label on to a piece of paper and then glue the foods on to the correct page, using the cards on page 35 as an aid. For children who can match the foods to the shops by the words alone, the pictures on this page could be masked before copying.

Developing Literacy
Non-fiction Year R
© A & C Black 2002

At the pond

- **Write the missing words.**

- **Show where the word goes.**

I ✔ to the pond.  went

I   some ducks.

There was   frog.

There   a fish.

- **Write each sentence correctly.**

They must all make sense.

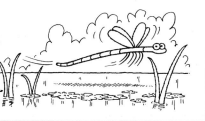

I _____ ____ _____ pond.

I _____ _____ ducks.

_____ _____ ____ frog.

_____ _____ ____ fish.

- **Write two more sentences about the pond.**

Teachers' note Enlarge the sentences and read them with the class or group. Stop after each sentence and ask the children if it makes sense. Ask if you have read it correctly and then check it with them. Discuss what the children could do to make sense of the sentences.

Developing Literacy
Non-fiction Year R
© A & C Black 2002

At the beach

- **Write the missing words.**

- **Show where the word goes.**

We went to beach. | the |

There was   crab.

There   a shell.

The sea   cold.

- **Write each sentence correctly.**

We _____ ___ _____ beach.

_____ _____ ___ crab.

_____ _____ ___ shell.

The _____ _____ _____ .

 • **Write two more sentences about the beach.**

Teachers' note Enlarge the sentences and read them with the class or group. Stop after each sentence and ask the children if it makes sense. Ask if you have read it correctly and then check it with them. Discuss what the children could do to make sense of the sentences.

Developing Literacy
Non-fiction Year R
© A & C Black 2002

Lunch boxes

• **Write the names on the lunch boxes.**

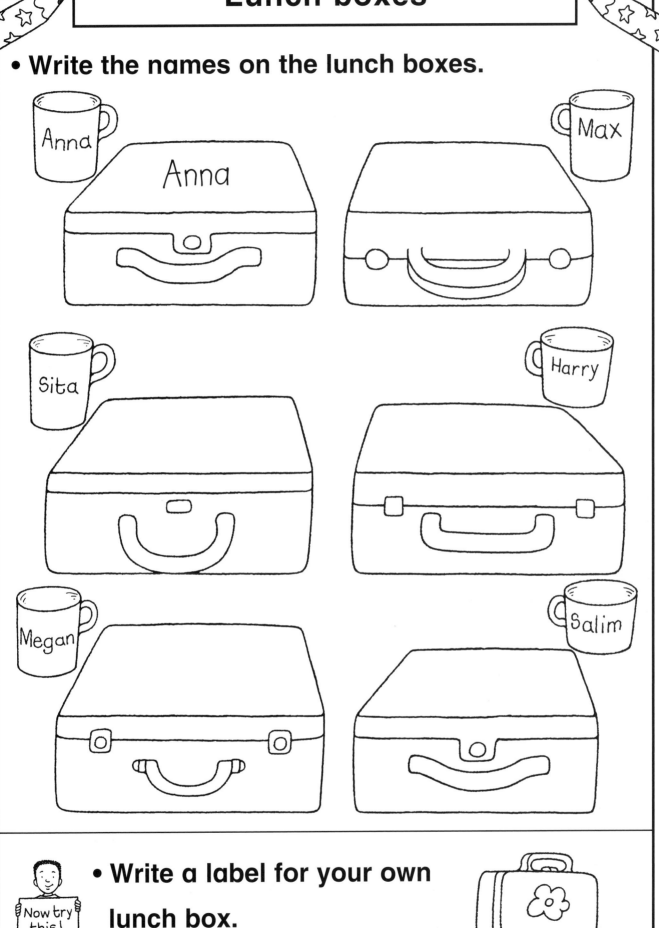

Anna

Max

Anna

Sita

Harry

Megan

Salim

• **Write a label for your own lunch box.**

Now try this!

Teachers' note This could be linked with word-level work on capital letters for beginning names. The children might not be able to read the names, but encourage them to say each sound.

Developing Literacy
Non-fiction Year R
© A & C Black 2002

Planting seeds

• **Write the missing words.**

Put some soil in a _____.

Put some _____ in the soil.

_____ the seeds.

Put the pot by a _____.

Now try this!

• **Write what will happen next.**

• **Draw a picture.**

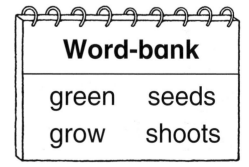

Word-bank

| green | seeds |
| grow | shoots |

Teachers' note After completing this activity, ask the children what they have learned about planting seeds. They could be invited to explain orally to the class how to plant seeds. As an additional activity, the instructions could be cut out and mixed up for the children to rearrange in the correct order. See also page 41.

Developing Literacy
Non-fiction Year R
© A & C Black 2002

Make a list

Jane is going to plant some seeds.

What does she need?

• Write Jane's list.

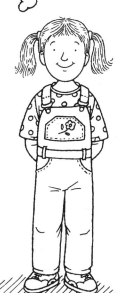

Plan how to make a model.

• Write a list of what you need.

• Draw pictures.

Teachers' note The children should first complete the activity on page 40. They will need to have that page available for reference. The extension activity can refer to anything the children have to plan; they could be encouraged, whenever this is feasible, to make lists as part of their planning.

Developing Literacy
Non-fiction Year R
© A & C Black 2002

Take a seat

- **Look at the pictures.**
- **Read the labels.**
- **Count the legs.**

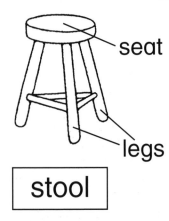
seat — legs

stool

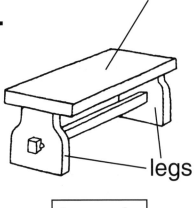
seat — legs

bench

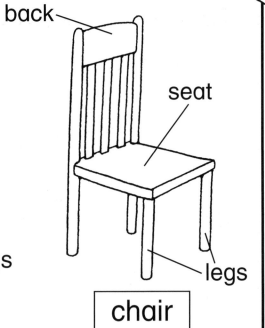
back — seat — legs

chair

- **Write the missing words.**

The stool has one *seat*.

The stool has _____ legs.

The bench has one _____.

The bench has _____ _____.

Word-bank

1	one	3	three
2	two	4	four

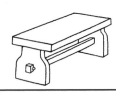

 • **Write two sentences about the chair.**

Now try this!

_____ _____ _____ _____ _____.

_____ _____ _____ _____ _____.

Teachers' note Encourage the children to use cues such as pictures and initial consonants to help them read unknown words. They could draw, label and write about other furniture (from either the school or the home), using the words from this page and others which could be provided in a word-bank.

Developing Literacy
Non-fiction Year R
© A & C Black 2002

Have a drink

- **Look at the pictures.**

- **Read the labels.**

lid

spout

handle

teapot

handle

cup

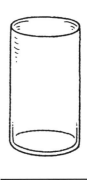

glass

- **Write the missing words.**

The teapot has a *handle*.

The teapot has ___ _____.

The teapot _____ ___ _____.

The cup has ___ _____.

The cup has no _____.

_____ cup _____ ___ _____.

Word-bank

| a | has |
| no | The |

Now try this!

- **Write three sentences about the glass.**

___ ___ ___ ___ _____.

___ ___ ___ ___ _____.

___ ___ ___ ___ _____.

Teachers' note Encourage the children to use cues such as pictures and initial consonants to help them read unknown words. They could draw, label and write about other crockery (from either the school or the home).

**Developing Literacy
Non-fiction Year R
© A & C Black 2002**

- **Write the words on the labels.**

Word-bank

door   gate   wall
fence   roof   window

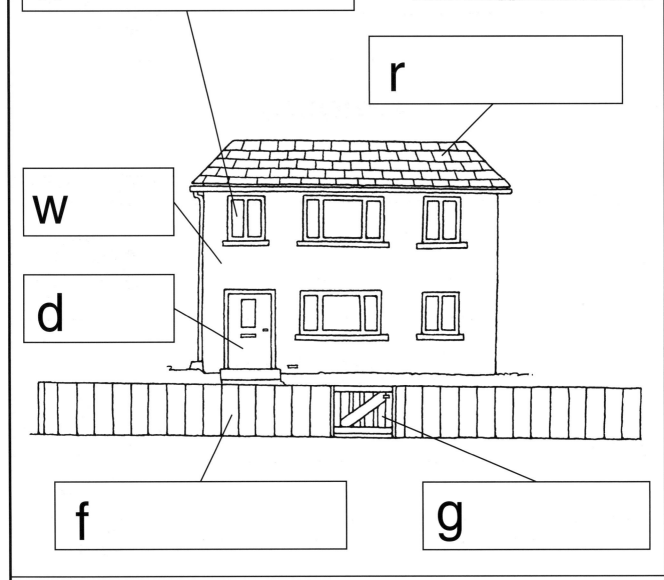

w

r

w

d

f

g

Now try this!

- **Draw your home.**
- **Write labels for your picture.**

Teachers' note When reading the word-bank with the children, focus on the initial phoneme and the shape of each word. Encourage the children to say the phonemes (where they can) as they copy the words from the word-bank on to the labels.

**Developing Literacy
Non-fiction Year R
© A & C Black 2002**

All about me

• **Fill in the** form .

Name _____

Age _____

Colours

Eyes _____

Hair _____

Things I like

Food _____

Drink _____

Pet _____

Toy _____

Teachers' note Encourage the children to use resources in the classroom to help them spell words, such as words for colours and pets. The aim of the activity is to provide the children with a format which encourages them to write for a purpose, i.e. to record information about themselves. Other forms could be provided in a role-play area, such as a post office, travel agency or bank.

Developing Literacy
Non-fiction Year R
© A & C Black 2002

up   down   over   along

• **Write the missing words.**

The cat goes _____

the tree.

The mouse goes _____

the wall.

The giant goes _____

the house.

Teachers' note Introduce or revise the directional words 'up', 'down', 'over' and 'along', perhaps during a PE lesson when the children can move in response to these directions. Continued on page 47.

Developing Literacy
Non-fiction Year R
© A & C Black 2002

• **Write the missing words.**

Up, down, along, over...

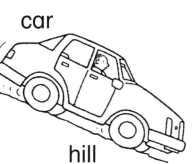

car

hill

The car _____ _____

the hill.

man

ladder

The _____ _____

_____ the ladder.

girl

path

_____ _____ _____

_____ _____ _____.

Now try this!

• **Where do you go? Write a sentence.**

• **Draw a picture.**

Teachers' note Continued from page 46. For the extension activity, the children could draw and write about the actions they do in PE, referring to the pieces of apparatus and how they travel up, down, along or over them.

**Developing Literacy
Non-fiction Year R
© A & C Black 2002**

In the picture

• **Write a sentence for each picture.**

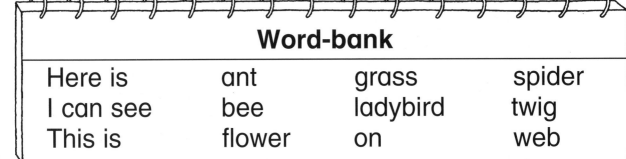

Word-bank

Here is	ant	grass	spider
I can see	bee	ladybird	twig
This is	flower	on	web

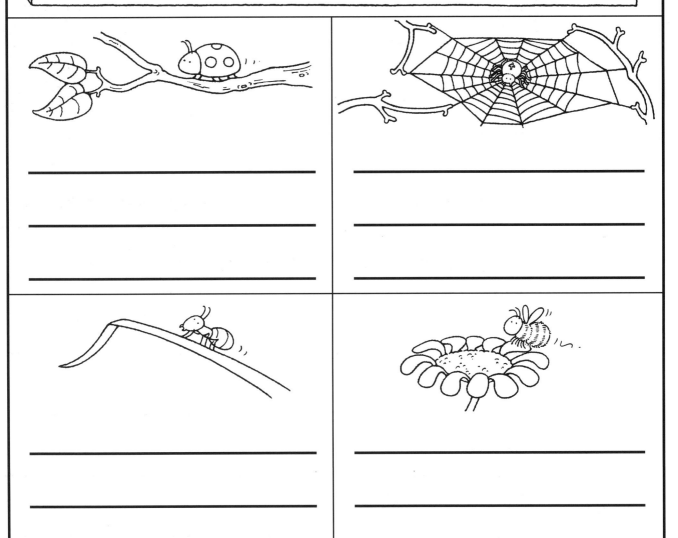

_____

_____

_____

_____

_____

_____

_____

_____

_____

_____

_____

_____

• **Think of another animal. Draw a picture.**

• **Write a sentence for your picture.**

Teachers' note Encourage the children to find the name of each animal by saying the first sound and then looking at the word-bank for a word which begins with that sound. They could also refer to information books or picture dictionaries. The children can choose how to begin each caption (using 'Here is', 'I can see' or 'This is').

Developing Literacy
Non-fiction Year R
© A & C Black 2002